DISNEY SQUARE ENIX

KINGDOM HEARTS

P9-CCR-543

Volume 2
Adapted by
Shiro Amano

HAMBURG // LONDON // LOS ANGELES // TOKYO

Kingdom Hearts II Volume 2
Adapted by Shiro Amano

Assistant Editor - Jessica Chavez
Copy Editor - Shannon Watters
Retouch and Lettering - Michael Paolilli
Cover Design - James Lee

Editor - Bryce P. Coleman
Digital Imaging Manager - Chris Buford
Pre-Production Supervisor - Vince Rivera
Art Director - Al-Insan Lashley
Production Specialist - Lucas Rivera
Managing Editor - Vy Nguyen
Editor-in-Chief - Rob Tokar
Publisher - Mike Kiley
President and C.O.O. - John Parker
C.E.O. and Chief Creative Officer - Stu Levy

A  Manga

TOKYOPOP and 🔄 are trademarks or registered trademarks of TOKYOPOP Inc.

TOKYOPOP Inc.
5900 Wilshire Blvd. Suite 2000
Los Angeles, CA 90036

E-mail: info@TOKYOPOP.com
Come visit us online at www.TOKYOPOP.com

Original Manga Comic by Shiro Amano
Video Game Developed by SQUARE ENIX/Jupiter
© Disney
Characters from FINAL FANTASY video game series;
© 1990, 1997, 1999, 2001, 2002 SQUARE ENIX CO., LTD.
All rights reserved.
Developed by SQUARE ENIX CO., LTD..

ISBN: 978-1-4278-1504-0

First TOKYOPOP printing: July 2008

10 9 8 7 6 5 4 3 2 1

Printed in the USA

KINGDOM HEARTS II

A scattered dream that's like a far-off memory. A far-off memory
that's like a scattered dream.
I want to line the pieces up... yours and mine.

Adapted by
Shiro Amano
Original Concept by
Tetsuya Nomura

2

CONTENTS

KINGDOM HEARTS II

WE ONLY HAVE TWO MORE DAYS OF SUMMER VACATION.

"HUH?" "WHAT DO YOU MEAN, 'HUH?'"

WE WERE SAYING WE ONLY HAVE TWO DAYS LEFT TOGETHER!

......

HUH?

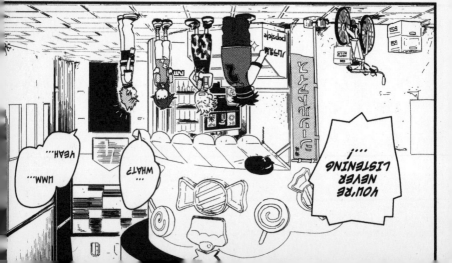

....WHAT?

....UMM....

YEAH....

YOU'RE NEVER LISTENING!....

WE'RE GOING TO MAKE THE MOST OF IT WITHOUT TALKING ABOUT SCHOOL!!!
OW!
OW-OW-OW-OW-OUCH!!
I--
I GOT IT!
I GOT IT! LET ME GO!!
WHAT'S GOING ON OUT HERE, BOYS?
OK THEN, DON'T FORGET IT.
GOOD!
HEY, LET'S WATCH HORROR MOVIES AT PENCE'S HOUSE ALL NIGHT!!
WHAT?! AT MY PLACE?
IS THAT YOUR IDEA OF MAKING THE MOST OF IT?
SOUNDS KINDA LAME...

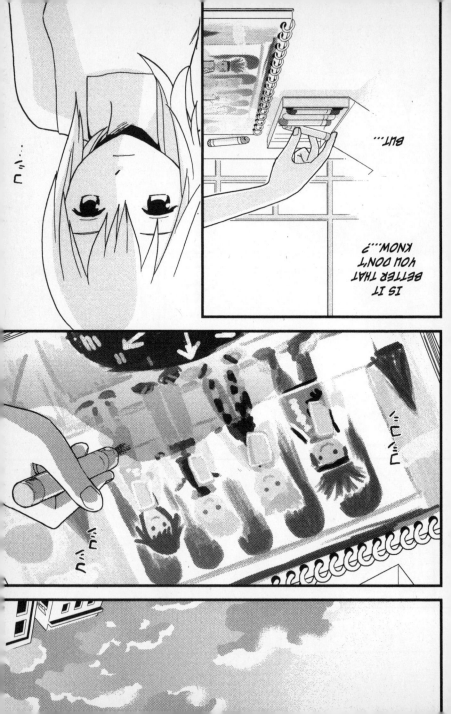

WHAT ARE YOU DRAW-ING?

.....

...HIS FRIENDS OF THAT WORLD...

ROXAS AND...

YES.

YOU'LL SEE HIM SOON.

IS SORA READY YET?

I'LL JUST LEAVE THE MONEY HERE!

WHERE'S THE CASHIER?

I WANT FOUR ICE CREAMS!

ANYBODY HERE?

DIS-
GUST-
ING.

YOU'RE GONNA LOSE IT WHEN I SHOW YOU.

I'LL HAVE TO SEE IT TO BELIEVE IT!

HEY.

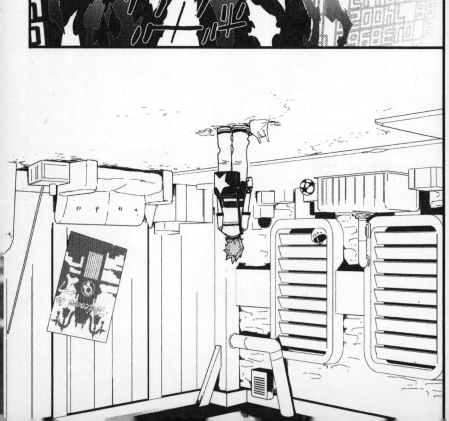

? ARE YOU CRYING?

· · · · ·

IT'S GOOD. TRY SOME.

HERE, I GOT YOU SOME- THING.

IF YOU DON'T COME BACK WITH ME, I HAVE TO DO AWAY WITH YOU.

I'VE BEEN GIVEN AN AWFUL ORDER...

UH, OKAY...

MAYBE I'M NOT SUPPOSED TO EXIST...

...I'M...

MAN, I WAS WORRIED FOR A SECOND!

WHOA!

WHAT THE--ICE CREAM?!

HEY, ROXAS....

ALL OF IT-- FAKE!

THIS WHOLE TOWN IS FAKE! D.i.Z CREATED IT!

THE ROXAS THAT I KNEW IS LONG GONE.

FINE, I SEE HOW IT IS...

ROXAS... COME TO THE MANSION.

THE TIME HAS COME.

HISS

YOU WERE NEVER SUPPOSED TO EXIST.

THIS WHOLE TOWN IS FAKE! DIZ CREATED IT!

Chapter 9: Shattered

BUT I DON'T HAVE THE KEY--

?!

GO!

...YOU'RE

...IT
OPENED
...

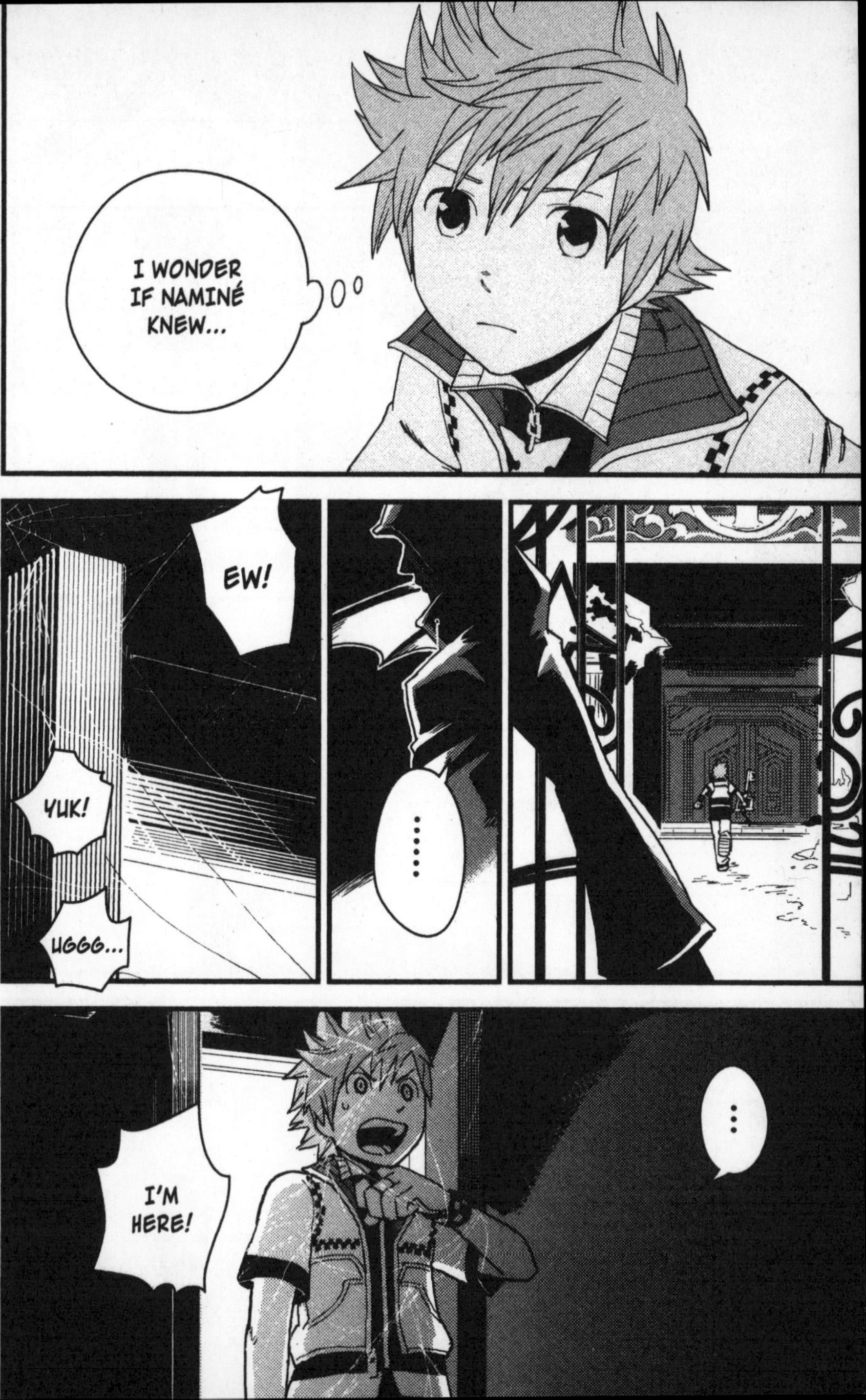
I WONDER IF NAMINÉ KNEW...
......
EW!
YUK!
UGGG...
...
I'M HERE!

STAY IN THERE.

CREAK...

WHAT DID SHE MEAN BY "DIS-APPEAR"?

......

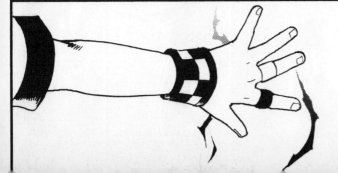

WHAT'S UP
WITH ALL THE
MACHINES....?

MOM.

A
CELLAR?

EVERY-
THING
WAS
BLANK.

I FELT
NOTHING.

....SPLIT IN TWO?!

WHOOSH

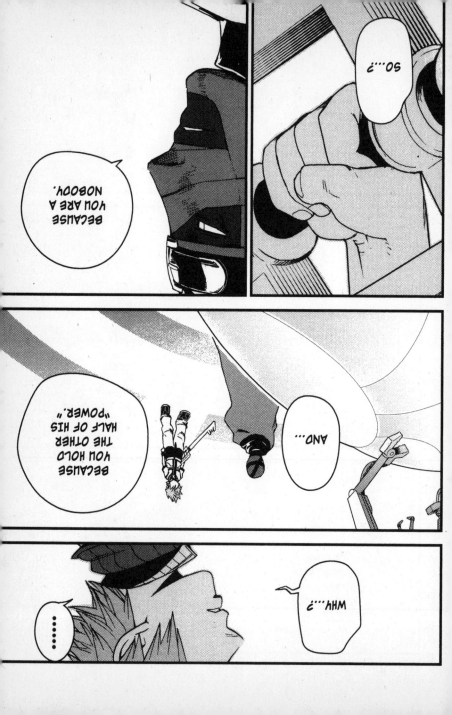

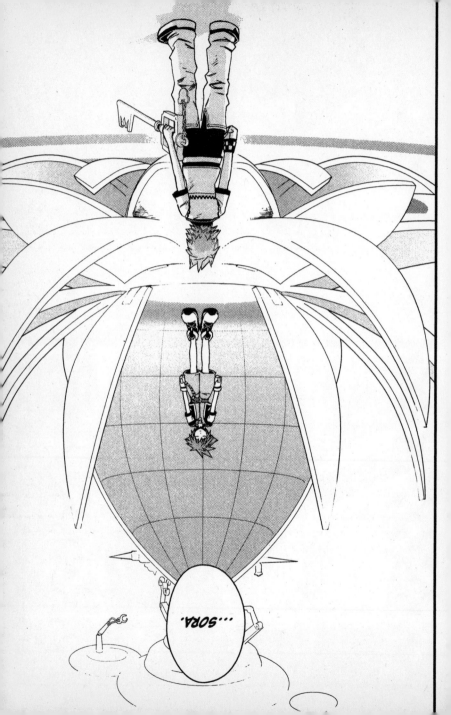

THERE'S ONE EXTRA.

HUH?

Chapter 11: Running from Nightfall

I THOUGHT I BOUGHT ONE FOR EACH OF US.

THAT'S WEIRD...

WHAT?

CAN I EAT IT?

ICE CREAM.

SUMMER VACATION IS ALMOST OVER...

AHHHH...

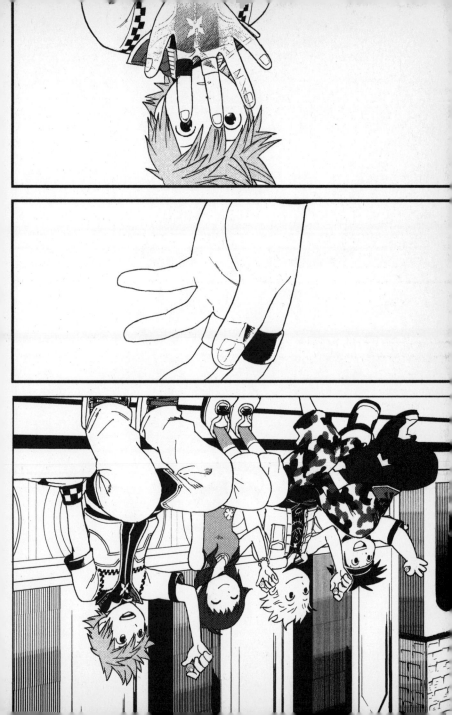

タタン‥

AH,
MAN.

I NEED
TO GET
A NEW
OUTFIT...

タタン

タタン…

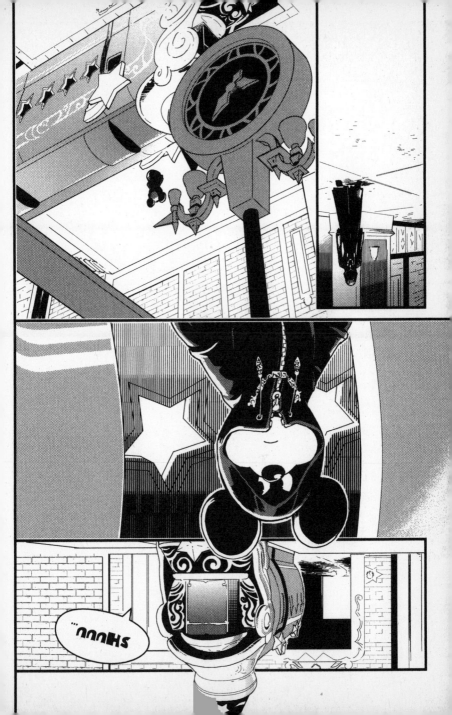

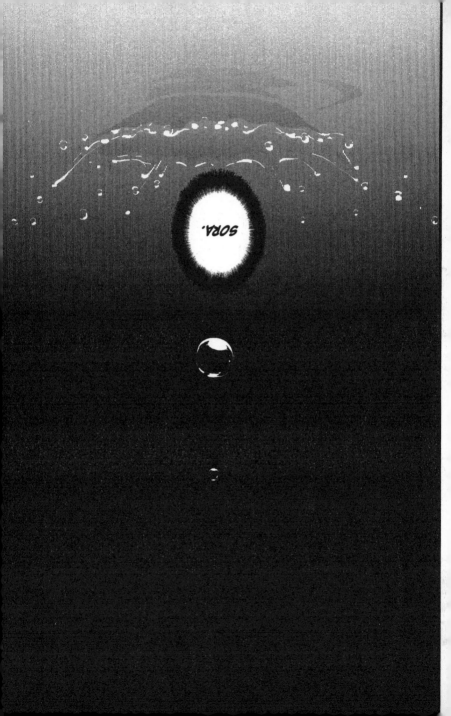

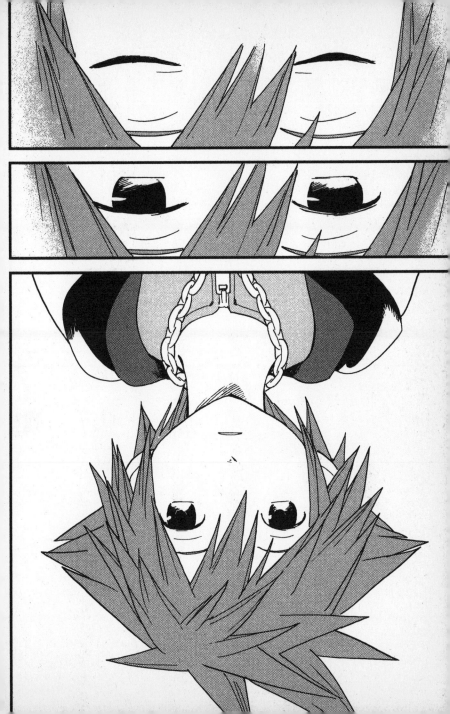

HURRY!

YOU NEVER KNOW...

RIKU AND KING MICKEY MIGHT BE NEARBY!

COME ON JIMINY, LET'S GO!

WELL...

WE NEED TO GO FIND THEM!

THAT'S RIGHT.

THEY'RE JUST TOO CAREFREE...

OH, WELL!

YOU DON'T KNOW WHERE YOU CAME FROM? NOW THAT'S MYSTERIOUS!

LET'S GET ON THE TRAIN. MAYBE IT WILL SPARK YOUR MEMORY.

FEEL FREE TO IGNORE HIM ...

MAYBE YOU HAD BRAIN SURGERY AND THEY REMOVED YOUR MEMORY.

WHY ARE YOU GRINNING...?

HUH?

?

YOU'RE KINDA WEIRD, DUDE...

WAS I GRINNING?

YOU, TOO.

WHAT WAS THAT ALL ABOUT....?

HERE, TAKE THE TICKETS.

....UH THANKS.

TAKE CARE.

IT'S BEAUTIFUL...

IT WAS IN THE BAG THE KING GAVE ME.

WHAT'S THAT?

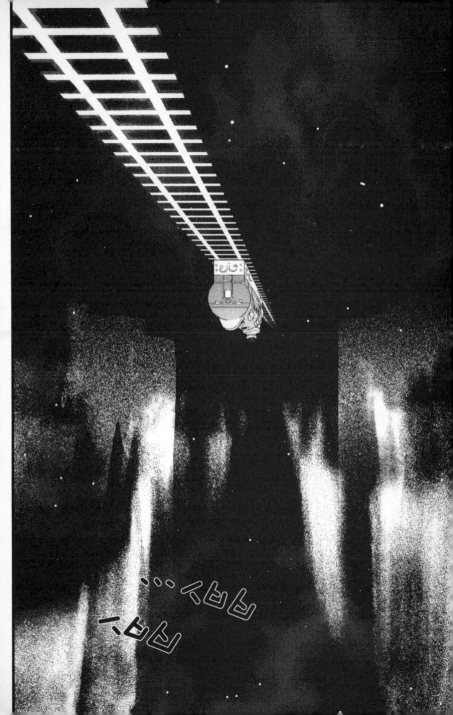

GO
GET 'EM!

CASTLE OF
THE MIGHTY
WIZARD,
YEN SID.

THIS
MUST BE
IT...

...WORLD
DOMINATION.

OUR
OBJECTIVE
IS...

WELL....

....IT MEANS HE STILL HAS UNFINISHED BUSINESS.

HE HAD TO LEAVE FOR HIS NEXT DESTINATION....

UNFINISHED BUSINESS?

YES....

....BUT....

DID YOU SEE THE KING?

YOU BOYS MUST BE TIRED FROM THE LONG JOURNEY.

...AND ATTACKS HUMANS TO STEAL THEIR SOULS.

A HEARTLESS HAS NO REASON...

WHEN A HUMAN WITH A STRONG HEART BECOMES A HEARTLESS...

MEAN-WHILE...

HEY, THAT'S MINE!

GET LOST!

...THE SHELL LEFT BEHIND DEVELOPS A WILL AND ACTS ON ITS OWN.

CORRECT.

JUST LIKE MALEFICENT WAS CONTROLLING THE HEARTLESS!

NEVER-THELESS...

I AM NOT SURE WHAT THEY ARE PLANNING.

...AND HE'S SEARCHING EVERY CORNER OF THE GLOBE TO REVEAL THEIR OBJECTIVE.

THE KING HAS SENSED A WORLDWIDE CRISIS...

KING...!

I CAN'T GO BACK YET!

SO THAT'S WHAT THE KING MEANT...

PLEASE DON'T STOP US!

WE'RE GOING TO GO HELP THE KING!

MASTER YEN SID!!

WHAT ABOUT YOU, YOUNG ONE?

SORA.

I KNEW YOU WOULD SAY SOMETHING TO THAT EFFECT...

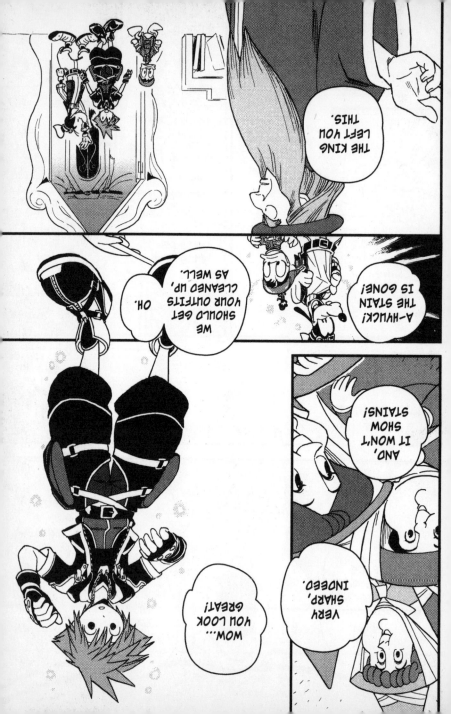

WE CAN TRAVEL ALL AROUND DIFFERENT WORLDS AGAIN!

WOW! IT'S A GUMMI SHIP!

...YOU WILL BE ABLE TO PASS THROUGH BY OPENING THE "GATE."

ALTHOUGH THE PATHS CONNECTING THE WORLDS ARE CLOSED...

GOT IT.

YOU MUST USE THE POWER OF THE KEYBLADE.

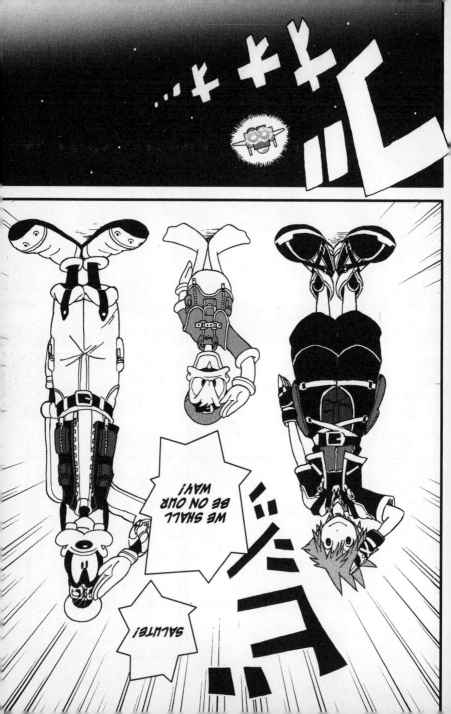

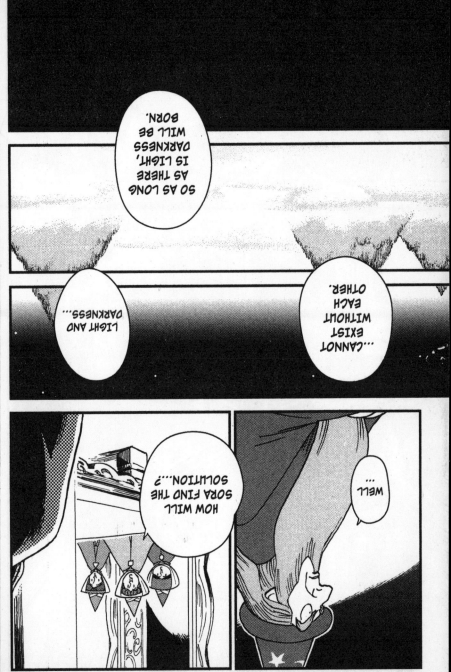

THIS IS THE ONLY GATE THAT'S OPEN RIGHT NOW.

WHICH WAY SHOULD WE BE HEADING?

LET'S SEE...

IT LEADS TO... HOLLOW BASTION.

THAT'S WHERE LEON LIVES!

...PEOPLE COULD LIVE WITHOUT FEAR, AND WE WOULDN'T NEED OUR WEAPONS.

IF ONLY WE COULD ACHIEVE PEACE...

OH, NO, NOT AGAIN.

I'LL GO TAKE CARE OF IT.

I GUESS PEACE MIGHT BE A LONG WAY OFF...

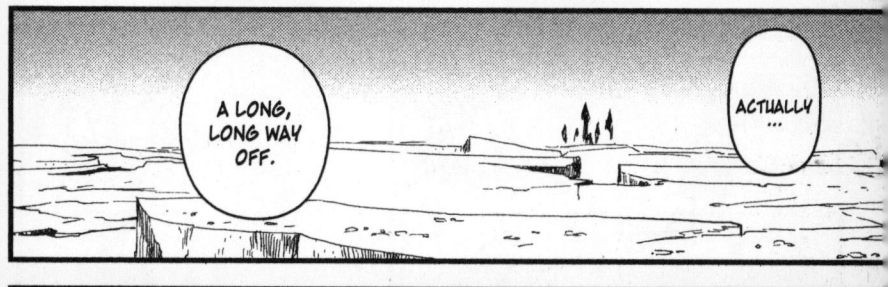

ACTUALLY
...

A LONG,
LONG WAY
OFF.

OKAY, ENOUGH WITH THE CLEANING.

VISIT THE WORLDS AND INCREASE THE HEARTLESS.

WHOA...

HERE, THIS SPELL WILL PROTECT YOU.

WHAT A WEAKLING...

I GET SICK WHEN I TRAVEL DOWN THE CORRIDOR OF DARKNESS...

THERE ARE SO MANY OF THEM ALREADY...

BUT WHY DO WE NEED TO GATHER SO MANY HEARTLESS?

YOU MORON.
DO YOU KNOW WHAT "WORLD DOMINATION" MEANS?
OF COURSE, IT MEANS ...
EVERY LAST HEARTLESS IN THE WORLD IS GOING TO BE PLACED UNDER OUR COMMAND.
CONSEQUENTLY, EVERYTHING IN EVERY WORLD WILL BE OURS.
...I ...

YEAH, IT LOOKS AMAZING.

THE CASTLE'S BEING RENOVATED.

BUT THIS IS OUR HOME.

WE'RE JUST PATCHING THE PIECES TOGETHER...

AND I WANT IT TO BE PEACEFUL, NO MATTER HOW LONG IT TAKES.

WE NEED TO FIND A WAY TO ELIMINATE THEM COMPLETELY.

BUT DEFENSE WILL ONLY GET US SO FAR.

YOU GOT AN ALL-NIGHTER TOO, MAKING THE ROUNDS...

WEARING THIS EXPRES-SION.

ALL RIGHT, I HEAR YOU.

LOOKS LIKE WE HAVE TO TAKE THEM OUT ONE BY ONE.

AERITH

SO WHAT SHOULD WE DO?

WE'RE SHORT ON MANPOWER FOR COMPLETE EXTERMINATION.

HERE, HAVE SOME BARLEY TEA.

カチャ カチャ

HOW ABOUT THIS STRATEGY?

BUT FOR EVERY ONE WE GET, ANOTHER ONE APPEARS!

AERITH! I TOLD YOU NOT TO PUT SUGAR IN MY BARLEY TEA!

MERLIN

THE OTHERS IN THE NEST WILL EAT THE POISON DUMPLING, AND WE GET THEM IN ONE SWOOP.

WE PUT POISON IN A DUMPLING, AND HAVE THEM TAKE IT BACK TO THEIR NEST...

HOW WOULD WE--

POISON DUMPL-ING?

!!
MEET THE HOLLOW BASTION RECONSTRUCTION COMMITTEE!
HEH, HEH.
LONG TIME NO SEE... EVERYONE!
HEY!
LOOKS LIKE WE FOUND OUR "BOMB"!

QUACK! THERE'S MORE!
DARN!
LEON!
!
COME ON KID, YOU CAN DO IT!
COME ON, CHEER HIM ON LIKE YOU MEAN IT.

HUFF...

HUFF...

HUFF...

HUFF...

WHO'S NEXT?!

SO?!

...WE GIVE UP.

WHO TAUGHT YOU HOW TO USE THAT KEYBLADE?

HEY, BOY.

DARN, I'M OUTTA DISK SPACE.

I SEE... THIS GOES HERE AND THAT GOES THERE...

WHAT YOU DID WITH THE CLAYMORE...

CIO...

I'M STILL WORKING ON THE OPTIMAL PLACEMENT.

YEAH, I WAS JUST WORKING ON IT.

カチャカチャ

ガチャ

HEY, LEON.

DID YOU STRAIGHTEN THINGS OUT?

I SEE—

バタ—ン

YOU WERE RIGHT TO PLACE THEM ON THE CASTLE WALL...

HEY!

To be continued in volume 3

What Dreams May Come...

Will Sora, Donald, Goofy and their
allies Leon and Cid be able to turn back the
hordes of Heartless in the canyon below
the town? Will they uncover the true
nature and intentions of the mysterious
Orginazation XIII? And will Roxas regain his
heart and finally join the ranks of the living,
or is he fated to forever remain a nobody?

To find out the answers to these
questions and more, you'll have
to return for the next fantastic
volume of KINGDOM HEARTS II!

He is the wielder of the "Keyblade" and the one charged with saving the world. He was in a deep sleep, but he has awoken to continue his journey with the "Keyblade" to find his friend Riku and save the world.

S o r a

I PROMISED THAT I'D FIND RIKU... AND BRING HIM HOME.

Goofy

Together with Sora and Donald, he is searching for the missing King Mickey. Goofy is a cheerful character, and was also in a deep sleep, together with Sora and Donald.

Donald

He is a master magician who has been traveling with Sora in search of the missing King Mickey. Donald was also in a deep sleep just like Sora, but woke up at the same time as Sora.

WE NEED TO FIND KING MICKEY AND RIKU AND BRING THEM BACK!

WE'RE GOING TO GO HELP THE KING!

KINGDOM HEARTS

Disney · SQUARE ENIX